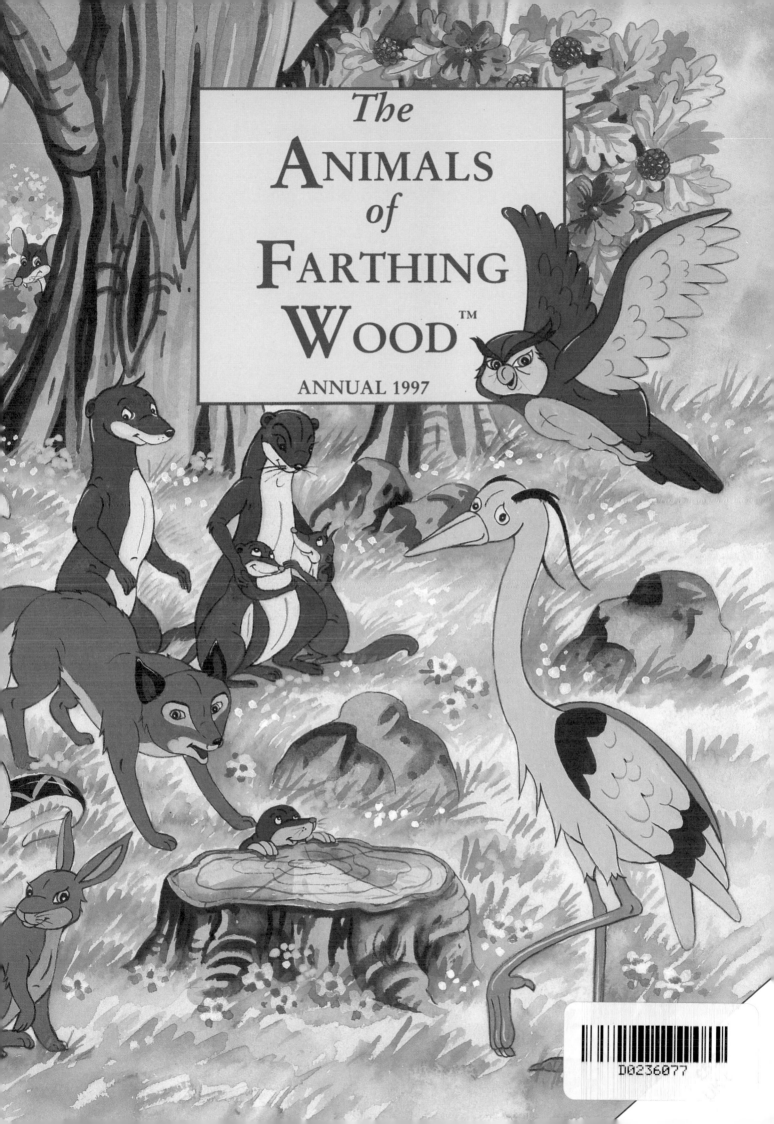

The
ANIMALS
of
FARTHING
WOOD ™

ANNUAL 1997

Contents

Written by Brenda Apsley
Illustrated by Jane Swift
Based on the novels by Colin Dann

From Farthing Wood To White Deer Park

Once, Farthing Wood was a good place to live. The animals who made it their home had everything they needed there – food, shelter and water. But when the humans came to Farthing Wood, with their diggers and trucks, saws and noisy machines, it meant trouble for them. Soon the trees and hedges where they lived were cut down, and the pond where they drank was filled in.

Now there was no place in Farthing Wood for the animals. They had to find somewhere else to live. But where?

Toad had an idea. He had been taken away in a jam jar by humans but had managed to escape. On his long journey back to Farthing Wood he had travelled through a big nature reserve called White Deer Park. "That's the perfect place for our new home, mateys!" Toad told the others.

The animals met at the Great Beech tree that night. Fox was to be their leader, and Toad their guide. There was one important thing to do before they set off. "We must agree not to harm each other, even though some of us are natural enemies," said wise old Badger.

The animals each held up a paw, a wing or a claw and swore a special Oath of

Mutual Protection. "We promise not to frighten, bully or eat each other on the long journey ahead," they said.

Their journey was a very long one, full of dangers and adventures.

The Farthing Wood animals met the dangers of the city, like traffic and humans. They met natural dangers, like floods and fires. They were often hungry and thirsty, cold and miserable.

Some of them lost their lives. But the animals never gave up. Always remembering their Oath, they helped each other through the bad times.

As winter came and the weather got colder, food was hard to find. Some of the animals, like Toad, Adder and Mr and Mrs Hedgehog knew that soon they must stop for their long winter sleep. But they had to find somewhere they would all be safe.

Toad was the only one who was still cheerful. He somehow knew that White Deer Park was not far away...

One night Toad led the animals to a tall fence. He asked Squirrel to rub the frost off a big sign. Yes – he was right! He cheered as a picture of a white deer appeared. "We're here, me hearties!" said Toad. "We've got to White Deer Park at last."

All the animals managed to get under, over or through the fence.

"Well done, Fox. Well done, Toad," said Badger.

But there was no time for celebrations. The animals had to make new homes in the nature reserve before winter came. One by one they hopped and crawled, scurried and flew off to make nests and burrows.

At last, the animals of Farthing Wood were safe in their new home.

The Battle with the Rats

The red fox family, which had grown a lot since the animals had arrived at White Deer Park, was gathered in the Hollow, their usual meeting place. Fox and Vixen were quite old now, and enjoyed having their large family around them.

Early one evening, Plucky bounded into the Hollow followed by his friend Dash the hare. "Tell us the story!" he asked Fox. "You know the one!"

"Yes, yes," said Pace. "Please."

Fox laughed. "You must know the story off by heart by now," he said. "I can't think how many times I've told it!"

"That doesn't matter," said Rusty. "Tell it again, please!"

"All right," said Fox.

The young foxes gathered around him. They were still and silent as he began the story of the early days at White Deer Park...

"We Farthing Wood animals were settling in well," Fox began. "Until the Great White Stag, the king of White Deer Park, died. We all knew who was likely to take his place. Trey was the largest stag now, and a real bully. He soon made it clear that the park was for the white deer herd only."

Plucky couldn't help joining in. "Yes, Trey started to say that Leveret and the Rabbits couldn't eat the grass! It was for deer only!

Then he tried to stop me drinking from the pond! He said only deer could drink there!"

Fox carried on with his story. "It got more serious when the stream was poisoned by rubbish the humans had dumped in it. It meant we had no clean water to drink. Something had to be done."

7

Rusty could hardly sit still. "Don't forget the rats, Fox!" he said excitedly. "Tell us about Bully and the others!"

"I was just coming to them," said Fox. "Our trouble with Trey suited the rats very well indeed. They had plans of their own – plans to take over White Deer Park. Bully and Brat Rat were really nasty. None of us were safe from them. They tried to kill Mossy the mole and they would have if Measly the weasel hadn't saved him."

Vixen joined in the story. "There were more and more rats to deal with," she told the young cubs sitting at her feet. "And when Owl and the weasels left the park we knew we'd have a lot of trouble with them."

"A meeting was called to decide how we could deal with Trey and the rats," Fox went on. "Vixen and I tried to reason with Trey, but it was no use. He was stubborn and kept saying that White Deer Park was for the deer only. He said there was no place for us. And the rats were a real danger now. Even though we killed some, there were always more and more of them to deal with. Bully said that because there were so many of them they would win in the end and take over. I have to admit, there were times when I thought he might be right."

"What about what happened to me?" said Plucky. "Don't leave that bit out!"

Fox smiled. "Well, we weren't sure what

had happened to you at the time," said Fox. "We just knew you were missing. Dash thought she had seen you taken away in a cage in a van by some humans. When we saw the Warden taking away some other animals in cages, we didn't know what to think. We trusted him. We sent Whistler the heron to fly after one of the vans to find out what was happening."

Plucky took up his part of the story. "I met Whistler," he said. "I told him that the men had taken me to a new park to live. They were worried that there were too many animals in White Deer Park so they were moving some animals to a new sanctuary. I knew I'd be safe there, but I missed the other animals and my family. And I was worried about the rats and Trey."

Fox carried on with the story. "Ranger led the other foxes in a fight against the rats, but for every one we killed, three more took its place. Adder and her mate, Sinuous, did well, but they couldn't do enough on their own. And the rats were killing off all the frogs at the pond, which upset Toad."

Pace knew this bit of the story. "Tell us about when the rats attacked Adder, and how Plucky came to her rescue!" he cried.

Fox held up his paw. "All in good time, Pace," he said. "Plucky had hitched a lift on one of the sanctuary's jeeps and was back in White Deer Park not a moment too soon. The rats set a trap for Adder, and Plucky managed to save her. but the rats swore they would have their revenge.

Meanwhile, I had another idea. My plan was that we would get the humans to help us. We killed as many rats as we could by night and left them outside the Warden's cottage. We hoped he would wonder what was happening and do something about the rats."

Fox paused to get his breath. Lots of gleaming black eyes were turned to him as night fell and the story continued. "But the Warden didn't act fast enough. And though we didn't know it, Bully had plans of his own. He and Spike and some of the other rats planned to kill Adder in her sleeping place. But one snake looks much the same to a rat, and they killed Sinuous instead. There was nothing we could do to help him." Fox paused. "Or Toad. He confronted Bully when the rats attacked the frogs again. This time they attacked him. The deer herd helped us, and their hooves scattered the rats. Whistler carried Toad back here to the Hollow, but it was too late. Our good friend died. Without him there would have been no journey, no new home for us here in White Deer Park. But his death gave us the heart to fight on."

The young foxes were quiet as Fox paused and thought of his old friend. "Toad's brave end gave us all courage," he continued. "We confronted Trey at the pond and he backed off for once. I started to think we might be getting somewhere. But then the great storm came. We went into Badger's old set and as many of us as possible sheltered underground.

do but hope the Warden would find him and help him."

One of the tiny fox cubs spoke up. "Is this the part where Weasel and Measly came back with their new family?" he asked.

Fox nodded. "Yes, and we were very glad to see them. Weasel was angry when she heard what had happened to Toad, and she decided to teach the rats a lesson. Another bit of good news was that Trey's place was taken by Laird, one of the Great White Stag's grandsons. He was very different to Trey, and he promised to help us in our battle against the rats. And then Owl came back to the park with her mate, Hollow. They saw a huge horde of rats getting ready for battle and overheard Bully's plan. Now we knew what to expect.

"The rat attack came at dawn. We had all been sleeping, and were taken by surprise at first. They were vicious and brutal. But

We could hear the terrible damage the storm was doing, and we wondered how the rats were faring."

"The strong wind tore down part of the fence and Trey saw his chance to get rid of the other stags. He picked a fight with one and in the tussle a tree that had been hit in the storm fell on top of him. I showed the deer how to roll the tree off him. Trey was badly hurt and there was nothing we could

11

we fought back. We foxes set about the rats with our snapping teeth. The Weasel family were a great help, and so were Owl and Hollow. Shadow, Whistler and Speedy played their part, too, in fact all the animals did. But there were just so many rats…"

Fox was quiet for a few seconds as he remembered the battle. "The rats had killed dear old Mossy." Fox shook his head sadly. "I have to admit that I thought about giving up then," he said, "but Owl gave me the strength to carry on. And, though we didn't know it at the time, help was on its way. Dash persuaded Laird and the deer herd to help again. Their flying hooves scattered hundreds of rats. The deer were too much even for Bully. He called on his troops to retreat, but not before Hollow's sharp eyes spotted him. Hollow swooped down on Bully and killed him. And that was enough for the rats. They lost their courage along with their leader and the weasels and owls chased them out of the park forever."

Fox looked around at the pairs of eager eyes. It was dark now. "Well, that was the end of the rats," he went on. "But not the end of the story. Laird agreed that we would all live in the park together, and then Whistler arrived with more good news. The fence was mended, but now it was in a different place. The Warden and his helpers had joined up White Deer Park with the other sanctuary where Plucky had been. Now we could all live together again in peace and safety."

Rats

Bully and his horde of rats wanted to take over White Deer Park. There were more and more rats for Fox and the others to deal with.

Look carefully at this picture of the rats.

How many rats can you count?
Where is Bully?

The answers are on page 61.

13

Spot the Differences

Look at these two pictures of White Deer Park very carefully. There are 6 things that are different in the bottom picture. Can you find them all ?

The answers are on page 61.

14

Owl's Story

1. Though she had a new home in White Deer Park, Owl had no mate. One day she flew off to Farthing Wood, her old home. Houses stood where trees had been.

2. Owl needed to rest. She flew to the open window of a dark attic room. A gust of wind blew the window against her. Owl fell to the floor.

3. She woke to come face to face with a cat! "There's no way out!" he told her. Then a boy came in. Owl flew down the stairs in a panic. She had to get out!

4. Human voices shouted, hands grabbed at her. Owl flew to a tiny window and just managed to squeeze out. She flew to a tree – the Great Beech of Farthing Wood!

5. Owl met a male owl, Hollow. One day Owl flew into some netting. Freeing herself, she fell into soft, wet cement. With heavy wings she flew up to the Great Beech.

6. As the cement set, Owl found that she could not move her wings! She could not fly! Hollow promised to bring food, but he did not know what else to do.

7. Owl looked like a stone owl. She grew very tired and thin. She spent a lot of her time sitting silently, eyes closed, thinking about happier times long ago.

8. Hollow felt helpless, especially when he felt the first winds of the coming hurricane. The winds shook the branches of the Great Beech. The whole tree shuddered.

9. Hollow spread his wings and flew away. The wind lifted him up, then threw him down into a hedge. Bruised and hurt, he crawled under the hedge to shelter.

10. A huge gust of wind sent the Great Beech – and Owl – crashing to the ground. Owl landed heavily. The fall broke the concrete from her wings!

11. Owl crawled off to find shelter until the storm passed. She found that she could fly, and she and Hollow made plans to return to White Deer Park.

12. Owl was weak and frail and her wings were not as strong as they had been. But Hollow brought food, and soon she grew stronger again.

13. The journey was a hard one for Owl. She had to rest often. She showed Hollow the places where the Farthing Wood animals had travelled.

14. When they got to White Deer Park, Owl and Hollow saw Bully and the rats getting ready for their attack. They overheard Bully's evil plans.

15. When she heard what the rats planned for her friends Owl regained all her old strength and wisdom. "We've got work to do!" she told Hollow.

16. Owl and Hollow played their part in the defeat of the rats. And now, their adventures over, they have promised never to leave White Deer Park again.

18

All about Herons

Herons are large birds. They are mainly grey, with a white head and black edges on their wings. They have beady yellow eyes.

Herons have a very long, bendy neck. They need this so that they can reach under the water to catch their favourite food – fish. Their long neck also lets them reach all parts of their body to clean their feathers. They use their beaks like a comb. A heron's neck has 16 or 17 small bones in it (even a giraffe's neck has only 7!).

Herons are good hunters. They stand very still in water and wait for fish to swim close. Their long legs mean that they don't get their feathers wet. Herons use their long beaks to catch fish. They also eat eels, frogs and insects.

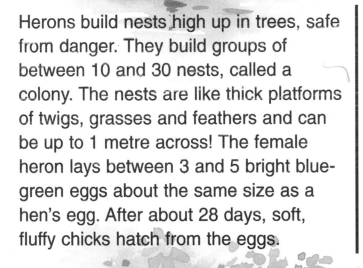

Herons build nests high up in trees, safe from danger. They build groups of between 10 and 30 nests, called a colony. The nests are like thick platforms of twigs, grasses and feathers and can be up to 1 metre across! The female heron lays between 3 and 5 bright blue-green eggs about the same size as a hen's egg. After about 28 days, soft, fluffy chicks hatch from the eggs.

19

The Trap

One day Plucky and Dash were playing in the copse near Shadow the badger's set. There were lots of conkers on the ground. They had fallen from the big chestnut tree. Plucky and Dash were taking turns to use a thick branch like a bat to hit the conkers. They wanted to see who could hit the conkers the furthest.

Dash had just made a big hit that had made her conker sail away into the distance. But Plucky was determined to win the game, and he got ready for a really big hit. But just as he was about to hit the conker the stick flew out of his paw and whizzed up into the air. It came down among some dense undergrowth. As it landed Plucky and Dash heard not a soft thud, but a loud snapping sound, like the sharp sound of metal on metal. They looked at each other in surprise. What could it be?

Plucky was keen to investigate and he led the way into the bushes. Using his keen eyes and his even keener sense of smell he moved slowly forward. He didn't like the scents he could smell, not at all. Humans had been there.

Plucky nosed aside a branch and gasped. "Look!" he cried. Two metal jaws with jagged teeth had snapped shut around the stick. Plucky tried to pull it free, but it was held fast.

Dash was right behind him. She drew in her breath quickly. "A trap!" she said.

The two friends heard a snuffling and a shuffling behind them and turned around quickly. It wasn't a human, as they had feared, but the kind face of Shadow. "Hello, you two, what are you

doing in here?" she asked.

Plucky didn't answer, but looked towards the trap.

"Oh, my!" said Shadow. "I saw one of those once, a long time ago, before Bold told me about this place, and I came to live here. A badger friend of mine was trapped in it. It caught him by the leg. There was nothing we could do to help him…"

"But who would set a nasty trap like this in White Deer Park?" said Dash indignantly. "This is a nature reserve. It's supposed to be a safe place for us animals to live."

Plucky decided what to do. "We must tell Fox," he said. "He'll know what to do. We'll mark the trap with that tall twig, so we can find this thing again. Come on."

Fox was disturbed and angry when he heard about the trap that had been set for Shadow. "Plucky, Dash, you two go and warn everyone about the trap. If there's one set in the park, there are likely to be more. Make sure that everyone takes extra care and keeps their eyes open," he said.

"Tell everyone to meet in the Hollow at dusk. Shadow, you come with me and show me where the trap is."

By the time Fox had seen the trap for himself he knew what had to be done. "We have to find out who is setting traps," he told the others when they gathered in the Hollow.

"Bad humans set them at night," Shadow told him. "The one who set that trap Plucky and Dash found will be back tonight, to check if he's caught anything."

"This is a job for us," said Owl, pointing to her mate, Hollow. "We'll watch silently from the the chestnut tree."

That night, most of the animals were quiet and still in the safety of their homes.

But Fox and Vixen and some of the red fox family waited silently outside the earth. Owl and Hollow sat high in the chestnut tree, as they had promised. Their only movement was the odd blink of their big eyes.

The moon and a few stars were the only light that night, but Owl and Hollow could see well, even in the dark. Sure enough, they soon spotted a dark shape moving through the trees. It was a man, and he moved very quietly, but not so quietly that their keen ears did not hear him.

Owl and Hollow watched as the man went into the undergrowth and pulled aside some branches. "Damn!" he swore as he picked up the trap and saw that it was not a badger that was caught in its vicious teeth, but a branch. Owl and Hollow watched, unblinking, as the man set the trap again and moved off into the dark wood.

Owl flew back to where Fox and the others were waiting. "Follow me!" she whispered, and flew off low through the trees, the fox family padding silently behind, eyes gleaming in the moonlight. Owl led them to the trap, and Plucky marked its position with another tall branch. Then Owl led them on to where the man had gone. The foxes' noses twitched. They could smell the man, even though they could not see him, and it was not a good smell.

When Owl, Hollow and the foxes got back to the den they had watched the man set six traps. They had marked them all. "We'll spring them safely at daybreak,"

Fox told them. "That way they won't be able to harm any of the animals."

Vixen shuddered. "But the man will be back, won't he?" she said quietly. "As many times as we spring the traps, he'll set them again. Someone is bound to get caught in one of them sooner or later."

Fox had to agree. It was good that they knew about the traps, but what they had to do was to get rid of them – for good.

Shadow stepped forward. "I think this is a job for the humans," she said.

Fox and the others looked puzzled, so she explained. "We must let the Warden know about the traps. He's the only one who can get rid of them for good."

"That's right!" said Plucky. "But how can we let him know what's happening?"

Shadow had an answer. "We'll get Sam, the sheepdog who lives at the Warden's cottage, to help us. I've got a plan that I think will work. We'll need lots of balls of that strong string and twine that the Warden keeps in the shed – and lots of barking!"

Weasel and Measly arrived. They had met Sam when they had gone to live outside White Deer Park for a while, and trusted him. "Sam's the one to help," Measly told them. "Let's all go and talk to him at dawn."

The next night the plan was ready. Owl and Hollow waited high in the chestnut tree as the man crept through the trees again. He pointed his torch towards the undergrowth and smiled a nasty smile. He could just see the glint of his trap in the moonlight – and the gleam of two black eyes. He smiled again. He had caught a badger, by the look of things! The badger seemed to have dragged the trap further into some very thick bushes. The man took a step forward, leaned into the undergrowth and put out his hand to check the trap. At that moment Plucky leapt out from behind a fallen tree trunk and jumped at the back of the man's knees. He was knocked off balance and fell forward into the bushes. His hands caught in a web of twine and string that criss-crossed the branches and bushes. He tried to step back as the twine snagged and caught on his arms and legs and around his head. The more he struggled to get free, the more he was caught in a web of twine. He was held fast and could hardly move.

As soon as Owl had given the signal that the man had come near the trap, Speedy had flown off to the Warden's cottage. Sam the sheepdog started barking as loudly as he could. Soon a light appeared in the Warden's bedroom window. The Warden knew that Sam must have a good reason to bark like that, and he came outside to find out what was wrong. "What is it, Sam?" he asked. "What's wrong?"

Sam barked and barked and ran off a few yards away. Then he turned and looked at the Warden. It was a clear sign that he wanted the Warden to follow him, and the two set off, Sam following Speedy, who flew ahead.

When Sam led the Warden into the copse he stopped, surprised. There, amongst the undergrowth, was a man,

wrapped up like a parcel in string and twine. Sam barked excitedly and nosed at the trap. Now the Warden understood!

Soon the man had been taken away and as soon a it was light the Warden came back to remove all the traps and put them in a sack. "We'll make sure these awful things are destroyed later," he told Sam, patting him on the head. "I don't know how you got to know about the traps, but I'm glad you did. There's no place for them in White Deer Park."

Shadow watched from the darkness of one of the tunnels in her set. She hadn't really been caught in the trap, but had acted as a decoy to lure the man into the trap the animals had set. She would rest a lot better knowing that the animals were safe again.

The Fox Family Word Square

Fox and Vixen have a big family now. Can you find the names of Fox and his family in the word square? The names are spelled out forwards, backwards, up and down, so you have to look carefully!

Tick off the names as you find them:

- ☐ BOLD
- ☐ CHARMER
- ☐ FOX
- ☐ FRIENDLY
- ☐ PACE
- ☐ PLUCKY
- ☐ RANGER
- ☐ RUSTY
- ☐ WHISPER

The answers are on page 61.

Catch the Rats!

This is a game for 2 or
more players.
You need a dice and a
counter for each player.

THROW AGAIN

GO ON 3

MISS A TURN

START

GO ON 2

GO BACK 3

RATS	1	2	3
Player 1			
Player 2			
Player 3			
Player 4			

Put your counters on START.

Take turns to shake the dice.

If you throw a 2, move 2 spaces along the game board, and so on.

If you land on a space with words on it, you must do what they tell you.

Catch a rat by landing on one of the RAT! spaces.

Each time you catch one, tick a box. Use a pencil so you can play again.

Go around the track as many times as you need to. The first player to catch 10 rats is the winner.

GO BACK 2

GO ON 1

THROW AGAIN

GO BACK 4

MISS A TURN

5 6 7 8 9 10

Dash to the Rescue!

1. Dash was out and about in White Deer Park one day. She was in a hurry, as usual! It was raining and she wanted to find somewhere to shelter.

2. Dash rushed from the clearing and into the long grass. All of a sudden something fell right out of the sky in front of her. It whistled past her nose!

3. Dash's eyes opened wide and she pulled her head back in surprise. She screeched to a halt. Whatever had just missed her landed in the long grass.

4. Dash pulled aside the tall grass with her front paws. She saw two little ears and two big green eyes. "A kitten!" said Dash. "But kittens don't fly!"

5. Dash heard an angry cry above her and looked up. A sparrowhawk flew in small circles over the long grass. "Mine! Mine!" screeched the sparrowhawk.

6. Now Dash knew what had happened. The sparrowhawk had snatched the kitten in its sharp talons. It was taking it off to eat when it had lost its grip and dropped it.

7. Dash decided to help the little kitten. It looked lost and shocked. She held the kitten gently in her mouth as she had seen mother cats do, and hurried off.

8. The sparrowhawk cried out in anger. "Craaa!" it said. It swooped down on Dash and the kitten, once, twice, but she was too fast, even for a hawk.

9. Dash carried the kitten to the bank where Shadow the badger had her set. Shadow laid the kitten on some soft grass just inside one of the tunnels.

10. Shadow stroked the kitten gently, and soon he looked a bit more cheerful. "He's better now," said Shadow. "But he needs milk if he's going to survive."

11. Just then along came Dash's friend, Plucky. She told him about the kitten and the sparrowhawk. "Where can we get milk for him?" asked Dash.

12. Plucky had an idea. He and Dash collected lots of twigs and made a sort of flat bed. They piled soft leaves and mosses and feathers on top.

13. Shadow put the kitten on the bed and they set off, each carrying one end. They carried the bed to the Warden's cottage and put it outside his door.

14. Dash climbed up on to Plucky's back. Now she was tall enough to ring the doorbell! Ding, dong! She leapt down and they both ran off to hide.

15. The Warden was amazed to find a kitten outside his front door. "Well I never!" he said, picking up the kitten. "Where have you come from?"

16. The Warden's cat had just had kittens. He took the little kitten to his cat's box, and soon he was part of his new family. All thanks to Dash!

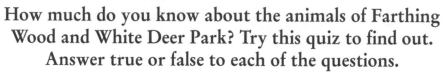

Farthing Wood Facts

How much do you know about the animals of Farthing Wood and White Deer Park? Try this quiz to find out. Answer true or false to each of the questions.

Check your answers on page 61.

1 Sinuous was Adder's mate. True or false?

2 Mossy's father was called Moley. True or false?

3 When the animals started out on their journey from Farthing Wood, they set off from a tree called the Great Oak. True or false?

4 Bully was the leader of the rats at White Deer Park. True or false?

5 A stag called Lonely took the place of Trey as leader of the White Deer Park herd. True or false?

6 Frog was the animal who told the Farthing Wood animals about White Deer Park and guided them there. True or false?

7 Dash is a rabbit. True or false?

8 The donkey that Weasel and Measly met on their travels was called Colonel Donk. True or false?

9 Friendly was the fox who met the old badger, Shadow, and told her all about White Deer Park. True or false?

10 Whistler is a swan. True or false?

All about Foxes

Red foxes are about the same size as pet dogs. They have a narrow nose, pointed ears and bright orange eyes. Their red-brown fur is very thick in winter, to keep them warm. Foxes use their very long, bushy tails like a blanket in cold weather.

The male fox is called a dog. The female is a vixen.

Foxes live in the open when the weather is warm enough. They rest and sleep under bushes, trees and rocks. They can climb trees and often rest in flat spaces between the branches. When it is cold and wet foxes move into underground homes called earths. They often use the tunnels of old badger sets or rabbit warrens.

Mother foxes give birth to their babies in underground earths in the spring. There are usually four cubs. The dog fox brings food for the vixen and her cubs until they are big enough to go outside and learn to hunt.

Foxes hunt mostly at night. They use their eyes, nose and ears to find food. Foxes hunt rabbits, voles, mice and birds. They also eat birds' eggs, beetles, worms, fruits and berries.

Animal Picture Crossword

Can you fit the names of these animals into the squares?
The picture clues will help you.

badger

deer

heron

owl

rabbit

rat

weasel

1. down

2. down

3. across

4. across

1. across

5. down

6. across

Wasps!

One morning Owl and Hollow flew towards their favourite tree. They had been out hunting all night, and needed to rest. They liked the tree because it was shady and cool, and because there was a hole in the hollow trunk that was just the right size for the two of them to sit in, side by side.

Owl flew into the tree hole first. Her keen ears picked up a strange noise, a sort of humming, buzzing sound. It seemed to be coming from inside the tree! She peered down into the hole and jumped back in surprise when some angry-looking wasps flew up out of the hollow trunk and buzzed and danced around her head. "Buzz off!" said one of the wasps. "This is our tree!"

Owl blinked. "I don't think so," she said calmly. "Here in White Deer Park we share the trees, and everything else." She pointed a wing at Hollow. "We always use this tree hole. It's as much ours as yours." Hollow nodded in agreement.

"Well, we wasps don't share our nest trees with anyone," said the wasp, hovering very close to Owl's face. "Now you two can buzz off nicely, or we'll make you buzz off. I don't know if you know what wasp stings feel like, but I can promise you, they're not pleasant!"

As he spoke the wasps danced menacingly around Owl and Hollow. They sounded very angry, and Owl could see their sharp stings.

"I'll say this once more," said the wasp. "Now buzz off – or else!"

Owl and Hollow looked at each other and, without another word, decided that the wise thing to do was to leave.

They flew off to warn the other animals about the new arrivals in White Deer Park.

35

Over the next few days the wasp became a real nuisance. One of the weasel youngsters was playing in the clearing. He peered into a bluebell flower. Out popped an angry wasp from inside a flower and stung him on the nose. Weasel complained to the wasps, but they just buzzed angrily at her. They flew round and round her head. "You keep your baby away from our flowers," said one of the wasps.

One day Whistler the heron was flying low over the stream. He wasn't looking where he was going because he thought he had spotted the glint of a fish in the water below, and was following its shadow. Suddenly Whistler heard a humming, droning noise that got louder and louder. His wings seemed to pass through a black and yellow cloud. He had flown into a swarm of wasps!

Whistler was in a panic and the angry wasps buzzed around him as his wings swirled the wasps this way and that. He felt sharp stings on his wings that made him pull them in towards his body. When he stopped beating his wings he fell out of the sky and landed in the soft wet sand on the bank of the stream in an untidy heap. Feathers fluttered around him and he lay his long neck flat on the ground, dazed and shocked.

That was where Shadow the badger found him. "What happened to you?" she asked. She knew that Whistler was clumsy,

but this looked more serious than one of his usual bumpy landings.

"Wasps," Whistler managed to say in a quiet voice. "The sky was full of them."

Shadow looked at Whistler's wings. Sure enough, she could see the the wasp stings among his feathers. "Those wasps!" she said angrily. They're a real nuisance! Since they arrived they've caused nothing but trouble. They think the whole park belongs to them. We'll have to do something to persuade them to behave better, or we'll have to get rid of them somehow."

Shadow gently pulled out the stings one by one, and soon Whistler was able to stand on his long legs again, though he was still shaky.

That night as dusk fell the animals met in the Hollow. Shadow told them all about what had happened to Whistler. Weasel told them about her baby's sore nose. "I'm keeping him out of sight," she said. "Those wasps are really nasty. Who knows what they

might do next."

Owl nodded wisely. "Yes, they're a real problem. We've tried to be reasonable and to explain that White Deer Park is for all animals, but they just won't listen. We managed to get rid of the rats, and now the wasps want to take over the park, just as Bully and his horde did."

The Squirrels arrived and overhead Owl's words. "Those wasps just chased us out of the copse again!" said one. "There's plenty of room for all of us, but they seem to think they are in charge. It's not fair, but who's going to argue with them when there are so many of them?"

"Not me, when they threaten us with their nasty stings," said another Squirrel. "What shall we do, Fox?"

Fox didn't know. "Perhaps we could reason with them," he suggested.

"We've tried that," said Measly. "They just tell us to buzz off. And if we won't, they'll sting us. They said that their queen wasp is the queen of the whole park and we'll have to do as she says."

Weasel had an idea. "Let's ask Sam," she said. "He lived outside for a long time. Perhaps he knows how to deal with wasps."

As soon as it was dark the animals went off to talk to Sam at the Warden's cottage.

They found him snoozing outside his kennel. "Wasps, eh?" he said when Weasel told him what was happening. "I remember there were some on the farm where I was born. The wasps were a real nuisance, so the farmer decided to persuade them to go off and make another nest somewhere else."

"That's what we ought to do!" said Weasel. "We don't mean the wasps any harm, we just don't want them to take over the park."

"How did the farmer get rid of the wasps, Sam?" Fox asked.

Sam told them, and the animals decided to copy what the farmer had done. Sam went off into the shed and came back with a wet sack. Then he sneaked into the cottage and came back carrying a little box in his mouth. "Come on," he mumbled.

At the base of the tree where the wasps were Sam found a hole that led into the hollow trunk. He could hear the wasps humming inside. He handed the little box to Weasel.

"The little sticks are called matches," he told her. "They make fire. You've got little paws. Pull a match along the rough side of the box and see what happens."

Weasel struck a match once, twice, then on the third strike it burst into flame. Weasel jumped back in alarm.

"Put it on the damp sack," Sam told her.

Weasel did as Sam told her, and soon the sack started to smoulder. It didn't burst into flames because it was damp. Soon thick grey smoke came from the sack. "Good," said Sam. "That's just what we need."

Sam took one end of the sack in his teeth and laid it over the hole at the base of the tree. Then he found a big thick leaf and swished it above the sack. It made more and more thick smoke.

The smoke started to travel up the hollow tree trunk and soon wasps came out of the top.

"Listen!" said Sam. "What can you hear?"

The animals

listened hard. Weasel spoke first. "Nothing!" she said. "No humming, no angry buzzing!"

"That's what's supposed to happen," said Sam. "I don't know how, but smoke seems to calm the wasps and stop them being so angry."

As Sam spoke, more and more wasps started to appear from Owl's tree hole at the top of the tree. This time they didn't attack the animals, but just flew around quietly together. More and more came out of the tree hole and when the swarm was like a thick black and yellow cloud, it moved off.

The animals watched as the swarm of wasps moved further and further away until it was just a tiny black dot in the distance.

"That's the last you'll see of them," said Sam. Weasel smiled. "Sam, you're a real friend. Thanks."

Sam looked bashful. "Glad to help," he said. "But I'd better get back. The Warden might wonder where his matches are, and I've got to drop this sack in the water bucket so it doesn't start a real fire."

Sam held the matches and a corner of the sack in his teeth and ran off.

"Thanks again, Sam!" the animals said.

Soon the copse was quiet and still again as the animals moved away.

Up in the hollow tree Owl and Hollow sat in their tree hole. Things were back to normal in White Deer Park.

39

Chocolate Marzipan Wasps

Why not make some wasps that you can eat?
They are quite safe, as they have no stings!

To make them you will need:

block of yellow marzipan

cocoa powder

chocolate buttons

currants

greaseproof paper

sieve

fork

Remember: never use the kitchen without asking a grown-up first!

2. Break off a little piece of marzipan, about the size of a marble. Roll it into a smooth ball between the palms of your hands. Press the ball on to a piece of greaseproof paper so that it has a flat base.

1. Wash your hands. They must be **very** clean.

4. Carefully lift off the fork. Your wasp has brown furry stripes now!

3. Give the wasp some stripes. Put about 1 tablespoon of cocoa powder into a sieve. Put a fork across the marzipan ball. Shake the sieve gently so that cocoa powder covers the marzipan ball.

6. Push two little currants into one end of the wasp for eyes.

Make lots more wasps in the same way. They are fun to make – and even more fun to eat!

5. Push a chocolate button into each side of the wasp. These are his wings.

BUZZ BUZZ BUZZ BUZZ BUZZ

41

Gone Fishing

Whistler and Speedy are fishing in the stream.

Whistler catches the fish that have **blue** fins and are swiming **left to right**.

Speedy catches the fish that have **red** fins and are swimming **right to left**.

How many fish do Whistler and Speedy catch?

The answers are on page 61.

All about Badgers

Badgers are about the same size as a medium sized dog. They have thick grey-black fur on their bodies. They have black and white stripes of fur on their heads and faces.

Badgers like to live in groups. They sleep and rest during the day and come out at night to play and to look for food. Badgers do not have good eyesight, but they use smell and hearing to find food. They eat fruits and nuts – and lots and lots of worms!

Badgers live in a maze of underground tunnels called a set. They dig tunnels with their strong front legs and paws, which have five long sharp claws. There are lots of entrances. Places like little rooms, where badgers rest, are called chambers.

The male badger is called a boar. The female is called a sow. Babies are called cubs.

Two or three badger cubs are born in February. They stay together in a chamber lined with warm bracken and grass. When summer comes the cubs come out of the set for the first time. They learn how to find food and look after their fur, keeping it clean and tidy.

Flying South

1. One evening the weasel babies ran into the clearing where Weasel and Measly were resting. "Look! Look!" they shouted, pointing up into the sky.

2. Weasel and Measly looked up to see a big V shape that seemed to fill the sky. Their keen ears picked up the sound of hundreds of beating wings.

3. It was a huge flock of geese flying together. As the weasel family watched the flock turned to one side and started to fly lower and lower.

4. "They're coming down," said Measly. "They'll be heading for the pond. Let's go and meet them. I've never seen geese that big before. Come on!"

5. The weasel family rushed to the pond. They were just in time to see the geese land. As their big webbed feet hit the pond they made tall sprays of water.

6. Lots of other animals went to the pond to meet the new arrivals. Plucky and Dash were there. As night fell, Fox, Vixen, Shadow and the others arrived.

7. The geese were pleased that they were welcomed at White Deer Park. "We're Canada geese," the leader said. "We're flying south, away from the cold winter weather."

8. He pointed to some smaller geese. "It's a long, hard journey for the youngsters who were born this year," he told the animals. "We stop to rest and feed every night."

9. As she listened to the geese, Weasel thought of the big world outside White Deer Park. "That's a real adventure," she said. "I miss adventure here in the park."

10. Measly scowled. "Yes, but there is danger as well as adventure in the world outside," he said. "Remember those nasty civets we had to deal with?"

11. "Our journey is full of dangers," said the goose. "Not all of us will survive it. Some are too weak. Some fly into cables and wires and get injured. "

12. "The humans put up pylons across the countryside. If young birds fly into them they are killed. You should stay here, where you are safe."

13. Soon all the geese had eaten their fill. One by one they settled down on the bank of the pond to rest for the night. The animals crept away.

14. As dawn broke over White Deer Park the animals went back to the pond to say goodbye. "Honk!" said the leader. "See you all again next year!"

15. The animals watched as the geese flew up into the sky. They formed a V with the leader at the front and the sound of their beating wings filled the air.

16. "I'm sorry to see them go," said Plucky. "Well I'm not!" said one of the ducks who lived on the pond. "Did you see how much those big geese ate!"

Shadow's Set

When Shadow the badger first went to live in White Deer Park she used Badger's old set. As time went on she added lots more tunnels of her own.

Look carefully at the tunnels. Starting from the entrances can you find:

1. Which tunnel leads to Shadow's sleeping chamber?
2. Which tunnel leads to Shadow's food store?
3. Which tunnel leads to an angry worm?

The answers are on page 61.

a   b   c

Weasel's Story

Weasel and Measly's youngsters never tired of hearing about their adventures in the world outside White Deer Park. When the young weasels found it hard to get to sleep, they always asked Weasel to tell them the story. Though she didn't always admit it, Weasel was proud of her adventures and the dangers she and Measly had faced, and liked telling the story just as much as the youngsters liked hearing it!

One bedtime the young weasels tossed and turned. They had had a busy day playing tag, and they couldn't sleep. "Tell us the story," asked one.

"Yes, please tell us the story, then we'll go to sleep," said the other.

Weasel didn't need to ask which story. It was always the same one. "All right, snuggle up to me, and I'll begin," she said.

"Our adventures in the world outside White Deer Park started when the Great White Stag died and his place was taken by Trey,"

said Weasel. " Measly saved Mossy's life when he was attacked by the rats. Mossy was grateful, but Trey told Measly that he shouldn't interfere. When we complained to Fox about Trey, Fox said our trouble with Trey was our fault. We were annoyed when he said that, so we decided to leave White Deer Park and live in the world outside."

"Where did you go?" asked one of the youngsters.

"At first we lived in a barn on a farm not far from here," Weasel told them. "You two were born there. We had a good life there, with lots of food, but one night when Measly raided the hen house to get some eggs to eat, the geese and bantams told us in no uncertain terms that they wanted us out. So out we had to go..."

Weasel closed her eyes, remembering. "A storm was coming, and we had to find shelter. We saw an old byre in a field and went inside, where we met..."

"Colonel Donk!" said the youngsters together.

Weasel laughed. "Yes, that's right, the old donkey. He said we couldn't stay, until Measly and I got rid of the mice in his straw. That changed his mind – but only until the morning. When he came in from the field he told us we had to leave. So away we went. I was having a bit of fun with some silly sheep when we met Sam, the sheepdog. He was fed up. He didn't

like the sheep and they didn't like him. He wanted some action and adventure – just like me! I liked him right away, and said he could live with us as part of the family. I told him he could look after you two and protect us all. Sam said he'd like to."

Sam was as good as his word. That night he brought food from the farmhouse. He also brought news I didn't want to hear. Sam had met Dash and she told him

50

quietly. "So I didn't think he was around when the civet came back with three friends. But Sam saved us again. We found a burrow near the river and Sam brought us food in his blue bowl. You two thought the bowl made a good boat, and the next thing I knew you were out on the river, shouting and screaming as the bowl filled

that the White Deer Park animals were looking for us. I thought they were our enemies, so I told Sam to keep our new home secret.

"Soon after that Measly took you two into an old burrow while I looked for food. What we didn't know was that the burrow belonged to a civet. I came back to find him about to eat you lot for supper, so I led him away. He soon had me cornered, and I would have been killed had it not been for Sam. He faced up to the civet, and it soon slunk off. Sam had saved my life – yours, too, probably."

"Good old Sam!" said one of the youngsters.

"Yes, I know that now, but at the time I was so worried that I said unkind things to him and sent him away," Weasel said

with water. Sam tried to rescue you by climbing along an overhanging tree branch, but it snapped and he fell into the river, too. Measly and I saw a bridge further along the river and raced to it, but those civets were on the bridge, and soon they surrounded us. What we didn't know was that Sam had swum along by now, and was under the bridge. When he saw the civet leader's tail dangling above the water he grabbed it, and the civet ended up in the river, too! His friends rushed off to rescue him, so Sam had saved the day again!"

"Measly and I were amazed when we saw you two jumping up and down on some funny stones at the river's edge. But they weren't stones – they were terrapins, and they and their leader, Terence, had rescued you. What was sad was that there was no sign of Sam. We thought he had drowned."

The youngsters couldn't help interrupting. "Tell us about the piglet!" cried one.

So Weasel did just that. "You two soon found a new friend, a little piglet, and he had to come with us. We thought we had found a new home in a copse of trees, but we didn't know that someone else lived there too. He was a huge wild boar and he wasn't very friendly. 'Hoppit!' he told us. And then the piglet saw him. It was love at first sight. I persuaded the boar to take the piglet home to live with him and his wife and he agreed that we could stay in the copse for a while. But not for long. Soon we had to say goodbye and set off again."

"We hadn't gone far when the Great Storm came and we had to go back to the copse to shelter in a hollowed out tree trunk. The storm tossed it over, but we were safe enough inside. The copse was destroyed, and the wild boar's wife was killed. It was awful. When Measly suggested that we should come back to White Deer Park, I was glad to agree. We had to find somewhere safe for you two to grow up. I learned a lesson. The outside world is full of adventure, but it can be a dangerous place, too."

"I realised that we needed White Deer Park and our friends there. And when we got back, we found that they needed us, too, in the the battle with the rats. I was angry when I heard about dear old Toad's death, and set about teaching you two how to deal with rats." Weasel paused. "And there's one more important part of the story. When we got to White Deer Park we found that the Warden had found

Sam and nursed him back to health. He was living with the Warden, so that made this place just perfect as far as you two were concerned." Weasel looked down at the youngsters. "Do you remember that?"

But the young weasels had heard their favourite story to the end, and had both fallen fast asleep!

Sam's Jigsaw Puzzle

Which two pieces of jigsaw will complete the jigsaw picture of Sam the sheepdog?

The answers are on page 61.

1.

2.

3.

4.

5.

6.

54

All about Deer

There are lots of different kinds of deer. Some, like the reindeer, live in very cold places. Others, like the white-tailed deer, live in very hot places.

Male deer are called stags. Female deer are called hinds.

All deer have slim bodies and long legs. Stags have two antlers on their head, which fall off in winter. The antlers grow again in the summer. In autumn stags fight with their antlers, to decide which stag will be the leader of the herd.

The red deer is about 2 metres tall. It is red-brown in summer and grey-brown in winter. Red deer live in groups called herds. They are active in the morning and early evening. They eat grasses, leaves and buds.

The roe deer is about 1 metre tall. It is red-brown in summer and grey-brown in winter. It has almost no tail. Roe deer are shy and often live alone. They are active at night, when they feed on shrubs and leaves.

The Storm

It was late autumn in White Deer Park. The weather was cold and wet. Grey clouds filled the sky. Rain was blown across the park by strong winds. The water in the stream ran in strong currents. In some places it lapped over the edge of the bank and spilled on to the earth. The wind lifted piles of dry fallen leaves and swirled them around in the air. Old branches cracked and fell from the trees. The earth was so soft and squashy that tree roots were loosened and trees swayed as the wind blew hard against them.

It was a time for finding safe shelter under ground. That was easier for the smaller animals who stayed warm and dry in their nests and burrows, but it was a hard time for the deer herd. The best they could do was to huddle together among the trees in the copse and keep their heads down.

One afternoon the weather got even worse. The sky turned almost black and the rain came down even harder. Huge booms of thunder were followed by lightning that zigzagged across the sky, lighting it up for a few seconds.

The deer herd huddled together nervously. Some of the young deer shivered as first thunder peals then lightning strikes seemed to be all around them, one after the other. Their instinct was to run away, but Laird and the older stags tried to calm them. There was nowhere to run to that would be any safer than the copse.

The whole herd shifted as one very loud boom seemed to break right over their heads. A second later bright white lightning tore across the sky. Suddenly it hit one of the old oak trees in the copse. It was like a knife slicing through the thick trunk of the tree, and with a mighty creak and a groan the oak swayed, then toppled over into the heart of the copse in a flurry of snapping branches.

The deer herd ran in all directions to escape the path of the falling tree. Laird and the other stags tried to gather the herd outside the copse. Laird looked them over. He looked again. One of the herd was missing, one of the young stags. "Has anyone seen him since we came out of the copse?" Laird asked.

None of the herd had.

Laird bravely walked back into the copse. The oak tree still seemed to groan and creak as its huge trunk shifted and settled into the soft carpet of earth and dry leaves below where it now lay. What was left standing of the trunk swayed and creaked as its weight pulled against its roots.

Laird peered among the branches and twigs of the fallen oak. He thought he heard something, and listened hard. Yes, it was a voice calling quietly. "Help! Over here!" the voice said urgently.

Laird trod carefully, searching the ground. Suddenly he gasped as he found himself looking into the eyes of the young stag. He saw his head and his back legs, but the rest of his body was lying under the tree trunk. It had fallen on top of him before he had had chance to escape.

"Don't worry," said Laird, trying to reassure the frightened stag. "We'll soon have you out of there."

Laird called to the elders of the herd. "We must try to free him," he told them.

One of the older does spoke up. "How?" she asked. "How can we move the tree to free him? His body must be crushed under its weight."

Laird spoke quietly. "It's not as bad as it looks," he told her. "Because the ground is so wet and soft, the weight of the tree pushed the stag down into the ground. He's lying in a sort of pocket. He's trapped

The red fox family emerged from their earth and sniffed the air. Fox looked worried. "I'm sure that storm has done some damage," he said. "I think we should take a look around. Make sure that Shadow and the Rabbits haven't been washed out of their tunnels. And that the heron nests are all right."

Fox led his family towards the copse, where they saw the young deer still standing in a nervous huddle. One of them pointed into the heart of the copse. "In there," she said. "One of the young stags is trapped under a tree."

Fox found Laird and the other stags struggling to move the heavy tree trunk. "We can't move it," said Laird. He sounded close to despair. "Can you help, Fox?"

Fox looked at the young deer and pawed the ground where he lay. Like Laird, he noticed that the ground was very soft. That had probably saved the deer's life. If the ground had been hard he would have been crushed between the ground and the tree.

Fox had an idea. "Plucky, go and get Shadow, Weasel and Measly," he said. "Dash, run to

and can't move, but he doesn't think he has any serious injuries." Laird looked at the young stag's frightened eyes. "We must try to free him. We can't just leave him here."

For the next hour the herd tried to move the tree. The stags tried to wedge their strong antlers under the trunk and lift together. The trunk shifted very slightly, but it was too heavy to move. Then the stags tried rolling the trunk, but again, it was too heavy, and Laird was worried that they might injure the stag if they pushed too hard.

The deer had hardly noticed, but the storm had passed now. The sky was grey instead of black and the wind had dropped. Only a few scattered raindrops still dripped from the branches that enclosed the copse. One by one the smaller animals started to come out of burrows and shelters, holes and nests.

the Warden's cottage and bring Sam. Tell him to bring some rope." Fox turned to Laird. "We'll never move that heavy trunk. So we must try to move the stag instead. We're going to dig around and below him. That way we might just be able to free him enough so that we can slide him out."

Work began right away. Fox showed the younger foxes where to dig, and they used their sharp claws to gently move away the soft earth from around the stag. Shadow's big strong claws made light work of the earth. Bold and Charmer found logs and branches and stones to wedge under the trunk so that it did not shift and crush the stag.

When a lot of earth had been dug away, Weasel and Measly went to work. They wriggled their slim bodies under the trunk on each side of the stag, pushing out loose earth behind them. Then they helped the young foxes to slip more supports in place.

After a while the young stag was able to move his hind legs and his neck. When Sam arrived with the rope they wound it around his antlers. Fox lined up the stags so that they could bear the weight of the trunk with their antlers as Sam and Shadow and the foxes took the rope in their mouths and pulled gently but firmly.

Fox gave the command. "Lift!" he said. "Pull! Nice and steady now."

The young stags watched, holding their breath, as the deer lifted and the animals pulled. Yes, the stag was moving. Slowly, slowly, his mud-soaked body emerged from under the tree trunk, which stayed in place thanks to the supports.

The young stag's eyes looked panicked and frightened. His legs twitched. "Don't

move a muscle!" Fox warned him. "Let us do the work. Just lie still."

Slowly, slowly, little by little, the young stag was pulled clear of the tree trunk. Soon he was free. He lay quietly, as Fox had told him to, then when Fox said, "All right. Can you get up?" he slowly got up on to his feet. His legs shook and he still looked shocked and dazed, but he seemed to be not too badly hurt.

Shadow checked him over quickly. "No broken bones," she said. "Just a few scratches."

The older does moved close to the young stag, as if supporting and protecting him.

The whole herd seemed to relax now that he was out of danger.

Laird walked to where Fox and his family and the other animals were resting after their hard work. "Thank you, Fox," he said. "Thank you, all of you. We couldn't have rescued him without you. You saved his life. We are all very grateful."

"It shows what we animals can do if we work together," said Fox. "Trey wanted the park to be just for the deer. Bully wanted to take over the park for the rats. We remember how you and the herd helped us in our fight against the rats. It's only right that we help you when you need it."

"I believe that there is a place for all animals in White Deer Park," said Laird.

Fox and the other animals nodded in agreement.

Sam the sheepdog woofed. He lived with the Warden but felt he was part of the White Deer Park family, too. "Even me!" he barked.

Answers to puzzles

Page 13 Rats
There are 16 Rats.

Page 14 Spot the Differences

Page 25 The Fox Family Word Square

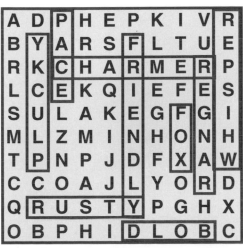

page 32 Farthing Wood Facts
1. true
2. true
3. false – the tree is the Great Beech
4. true
5. false – his name is Laird
6. false – it was Toad
7. false – she is a hare
8. true
9. false – it was Bold
10. false – he is a heron.

page 34 Animal Picture-Word

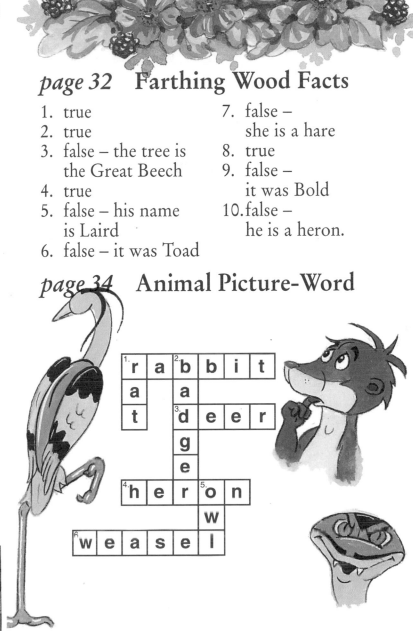

page 42 Gone Fishing
Whistler caught 5 fish. Speedy caught 6 fish.

page 48 Shadow's Set
1c, 2b, 3a.

page 54 Sam's Jigsaw Puzzle
Pieces 2 and 5 will finish the picture.